Elementary Particles

A SHORT HISTORY OF SOME
DISCOVERIES IN ATOMIC PHYSICS

THE VANUXEM LECTURES · 1959

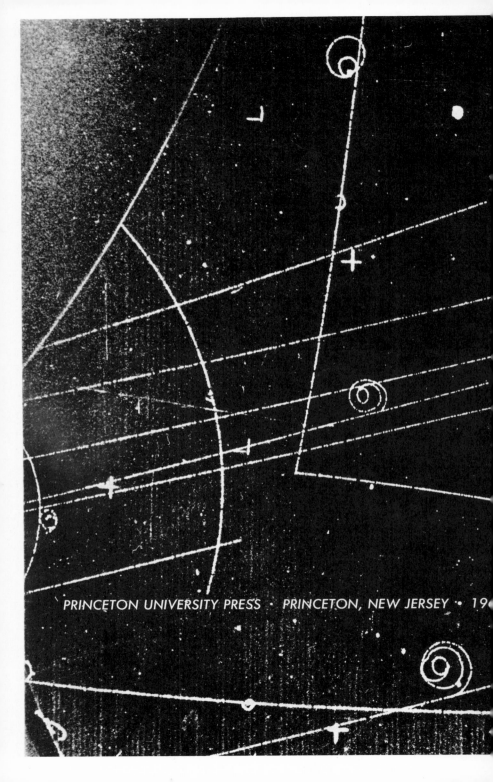

PRINCETON UNIVERSITY PRESS · PRINCETON, NEW JERSEY · 19

Elementary Particles

A SHORT HISTORY OF SOME DISCOVERIES IN ATOMIC PHYSICS

by Chen Ning Yang

TO MY BROTHER
CHEN FU

VANUXEM LECTURERS AT PRINCETON UNIVERSITY

1912. Vito Volterra
1913. Emile Boutroux
1913. Arthur Denis Godley
1913. Alois Riehl
1913. Arthur Shipley
1914. Sir Walter Raleigh
1915. Thomas Hunt Morgan
1916. Charles Richard Van Hise
1917. Paul Elmer More
1918. H. H. Goddard
1919. Maurice De Wulf
1920. Henry A. Cotton
1921. Chauncey B. Tinker
1922. Vernon Kellogg
1923. A. J. B. Wace
1924. Louis T. More
1925. J. Franklin Jameson
1926. Henry Fairfield Osborn
1927. J. J. R. MacLeod
1928. A. N. Whitehead
1929. Sir James C. Irvine
1930. Bliss Perry
1931. Edwin P. Hubble
1932. Theobald Smith
1933. Archibald Bowman
1934. Herbert S. Jennings
1934. Frank Jewett Mather, Jr.
1935. Percy W. Bridgman
1936. Heinrich Bruening
1937. David Riesman
1938. Thomas Mann
1938. Detlev W. Bronk
1939. Earnest A. Hooton
1939. Francis G. Benedict
1940. Everette Lee DeGolyer
1941. George W. Corner
1942. William M. Stanley
1944. Edward Warner
1945. James B. Conant
1945. W. Albert Noyes
1945. Lee A. DuBridge
1945. A. Baird Hastings
1945. Walter S. Hunter
1945. Arthur H. Compton
1946. Patrick M. S. Blackett

1946. Herbert M. Evans
1946. Griffith C. Evans
1946. George Gaylord Simpson
1946. Percival C. Keith
1946. Frederic Charles Bartlett
1947. J. Robert Oppenheimer
1947. George W. Beadle
1948. Otto Struve
1948. Karl von Frisch
1948. Robert Broom
1949. Walter Bartky
1949. Lloyd Morris
1949. Dylan Thomas
1950. Julian Huxley
1950. Sir Richard Winn Livingstone
1950. Hermann Weyl
1950. Thomas Seward Lovering
1951. H. Munro Fox
1951. John R. Dunning
1951. Karl S. Lashley
1951. Dylan Thomas
1951. William Carlos Williams
1951. J. Allen Westrup
1952. Wolfgang Köhler
1952. George Gamow
1952. John von Neumann
1952. John E. Burchard
1952. Ralph Ellison
1953. George Wald
1953. Ernest Nagel
1954. Linus C. Pauling
1955. Konrad Lorenz
1956. Wilder Penfield
1956. H. P. Robertson
1957. Arend Heyting
1958. Claude Shannon
1958. Harold C. Urey
1958. Francis Birch
1958. F. A. Vening-Meinesz
1959. Gordon MacDonald
1959. Roger Revelle
1959. Chen Ning Yang
1959. L. S. B. Leakey
1960. Edwin H. Land
1960. Tracy M. Sonneborn

THIS BOOK is essentially the Vanuxem Lectures that I gave at Princeton University in November 1959, with minor revisions. The lectures were intended for an audience consisting of university people with general interest in science. By describing in simple terms the ideas involved in the discovery of the elementary particles, I tried to delineate for the audience the general outline of the research work in the last sixty years in the exploration of the structure of matter. It is of course true that an idea, especially a scientific idea, does not have full meaning unless defined against a background of knowledge from which the idea originated and developed. It is hoped, however, that a descriptive history like this book may convey some impression of the spirit and the atmosphere in which physicists approach the problem, even though the subject matter cannot be adequately discussed.

A list of the sources of the illustrations is to be found at the end of the book. The horseman drawing on the dust-jacket, which also appears as Figure 39 in the book, was made by Mr. M. C. Escher whose kind permission for its use is gratefully acknowledged.

I wish to thank my wife for letting me try out on her the manuscript for understandability and for clarity of presentation. Her suggestions proved invaluable. I wish to thank Mrs. Elizabeth Gorman for the very competent help she has rendered in all phases of the preparation for publication of this book. It is a pleasure to acknowledge the assistance of Mr. J. F. Wilson of the Princeton University Press in preparing the figures, especially Figure 36, which derived from an idea of his.

CHEN NING YANG

June 1961

Elementary Particles

FIGURE 1

AT THE TURN of the century the world of physics was clearly coming into the dawn of a new era. Not only did the brilliant achievements of classical mechanics and of the Faraday-Maxwell theory of electromagnetism bring to a successful termination the era of classical macroscopic physics, but there were already in the air everywhere new phenomena, new puzzlement, new excitement, and new anticipation. Cathode rays, photoelectricity, radioactivity, the Zeeman effect, X-rays, and the Rydberg law of spectral lines were all recent discoveries. What the new era would have in store was of course difficult to predict at that time. Among other things, there was much discussion of the possible atomic structure of electricity. But let us recognize that although the concept of the atomic structure of matter had been speculated upon since early times, such speculation could not be entered into the books of scientific knowledge. For without quantitative experimental verification, no philosophical discussions can be accepted as scientific truth. For example, as late as 1897, Lord Kelvin, a giant in the world of physics in the latter part of the nineteenth century, still wrote[1] that the idea that "electricity is a continuous homogeneous liquid" (rather than having an atomic structure) deserved careful consideration.

Such considerations became unnecessary when, in the same year, J. J. Thomson performed his celebrated experiment which determined the ratio e/m of the charge and the mass of the cathode rays. I cannot resist the temptation of showing you in the first figure (reproduced from his book, *Recollections and Reflections*) a magnificent bust of the man who first opened the door to the physics of elementary particles.

FIGURE 2

Thomson's apparatus is shown in Figure 2, and is diagrammatically illustrated in Figure 3. Cathode rays from the cathode C were made to pass through the slits A and B, which served to define a narrow beam. The beam then passed through the region between D and E, and was observed on the calibrated screen at the right end of the tube. By charging up the plates D and E, an upward or downward de-

FIGURE 3

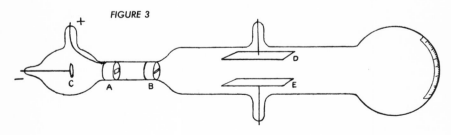

flection of the beam was produced. The direction of deflection showed that the charge carried by the beam was negative. Then a magnetic field was imposed on the region between D and E by the coils shown in Figure 2, the field direction being perpendicular to the plane of the book. It was observed that the magnetic field also produced an upward or downward deflection of the beam consistent with its negative charge. By balancing the deflections produced by the electric and magnetic fields it was possible to compute the velocity of the beam. The magnitude of the deflection produced by either field alone then gave a measurement of e/m, the ratio of the charge to the mass of the constituents of the beam.

It may be asked why it is that this experiment that seems so simple was not an obvious one. Thomson himself provided an answer to this when he wrote later,[2]

"My first attempt to deflect a beam of cathode rays was to pass it between two parallel metal plates fastened inside the discharge-tube, and to produce an electric field between the plates. This failed to produce any lasting deflection."

He then explained what he suspected was the origin of the trouble and added,

"The absence of deflection on this view is due to the presence of gas—to the pressure being too high—thus the thing to do was to get a much higher vacuum. This was more easily said than done. The technique of producing high vacua in those days was in an elementary stage."

In fact, no less a physicist than H. Hertz, discoverer of the electromagnetic waves, had tried the same experiment before[3] and had been misled to the conclusion that cathode rays were not charged. The episode illustrates most clearly an elementary fact that technological improvements go hand-in-hand with the advancement of experimental sciences. We shall encounter further illustrations of this basic truth later on.

The value of e/m Thomson obtained for the cathode rays was much bigger than the corresponding values determined for the ions in electrolysis, by a factor of several thousand. Thomson concluded that the cathode ray consisted of particles with a mass much smaller than the ions, and with a negative charge. He called them "corpuscles," and called their charge, which represented a basic unit of electric charge, the "electron." In later usage, however, the particles themselves came to be called electrons. Thus was born the first of the elementary particles recognized by man.

In other experiments around that time Thomson and his students also determined approximately the value of the electric charge $+e$ carried by the ions. Thomson then speculated on the fundamental question of the structure of the atoms and proposed the following picture: An atom consists of a number Z of electrons, each with charge $-e$, embedded in positions of equilibrium in a continuous distribution of positive electricity of a total amount $+Ze$, forming an electrically neutral atom. The mass of the atom resides in the positive charge distribution. Upon disturbance, the electrons, which are light and therefore easily perturbed, oscillate around their positions of equilibrium and thereby emit radiation. Figure 4 shows a drawing of Thomson's, taken from his Silliman Lectures at Yale in 1903, for the case of three electrons. Assuming a uniform spherical distribution of the positive charges, Thomson computed the frequencies of the oscillations of the electrons and identified them with the observed frequencies in optical spectra. In this way he came to the remarkably accurate conclusion that atoms were of the size of around 10^{-8} cm in radius!

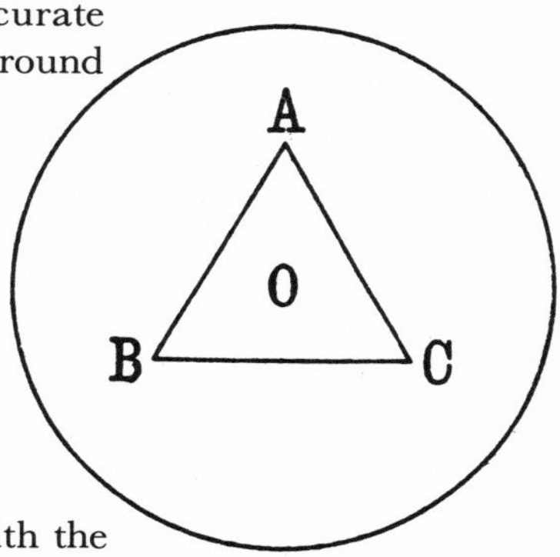

FIGURE 4

The next major advancement came with the study of Lord Rutherford in 1911 of the passage of α particles through thin foils of matter. The α particles were discovered in natural radioactivity and by 1911 were well known to be particles with a charge of $+2e$ and with a mass of four times that of the hydrogen atom. Thomson had previously pointed out that the path of an α particle through his atom would be mostly a straight line for the following reasons: (i) Because of its heavy mass compared to the electron an α particle would not be deflected by an electron. (ii) The influence of the positive charge in the atom on the α particle is also weak because of the spread-out nature of the former. A Thomson atom therefore cannot deflect an α particle through a large angle. Rutherford reasoned that any large angle deflection of an α particle through a thin foil, which naturally contains many atoms, would therefore have to be a statistical accident due to many single deflections in the same direction. As is usual in such statistical fluctuations,

(a) the deflection should follow a Gaussian error curve for large deflections, and (b) the root mean square angle of deflection should be proportional to the square root of the number of encounters, or to the square root of the thickness of the foil. Rutherford pointed out that neither of these conclusions agreed with the then available experimental data. He proposed instead, that the positive charges in an atom are concentrated in a very small region. In fact from the experimental data it was possible to conclude that the region must be less than 10^{-12} cm in diameter. This became the famous Rutherford picture of the atom consisting of a small nucleus of charge $+Ze$, and Z electrons around it, which a year later was given striking experimental confirmation by his students Geiger and Marsden.

The impact of Rutherford's discovery upon the physicists and chemists of those days was electrifying. Thomson was at that time at the Cavendish Laboratory in Cambridge and Rutherford was in Manchester. Niels Bohr, later in 1930 in his Faraday Lecture,[4] said,

"To everyone who, like myself, had the good fortune to visit the physical laboratories in Cambridge and Manchester about twenty years ago and work under the inspiration of the great leaders it was an unforgettable experience to witness almost every day the disclosure of hitherto hidden features of nature. I remember, as if it were yesterday, the enthusiasm with which the new prospects for the whole of physical and chemical science, opened by the discovery of the atomic nucleus, were discussed in the spring of 1912 among the pupils of Rutherford. Above all, we realised that the localisation of the positive electrification of the atom within a region of practically infinitesimal extension allowed a great simplification in the *classification of the properties of matter*. In fact, it permitted a far-reaching distinction between such atomic properties as are wholly determined by the total charge and mass of the nucleus and those which depend directly on its internal constitution. Radioactivity, which according to all experience is independent of the physical and chemical conditions, is typical of the last class of properties. The ordinary physical and chemical properties of matter, on the other hand, depend in the first place on the total charge and mass of the atom as well as on the electronic configuration round the nucleus, which is responsible for the reaction of the atom to external influences. Moreover, in an isolated atom this electronic configuration must be expected to depend almost entirely on the nuclear charge and very little on its mass, this being so large compared with the electronic mass that the nuclear motion to a first approximation can be neglected in comparison with that of the electrons. These simple deductions from the nuclear atomic model offered, indeed, an immediate explanation of the fact that two elements of different atomic weights and with quite different radioactive properties may be so alike as regards other properties that they are inseparable by chemical methods."

Again, later in the same lecture he said,

"Summarising the situation, we may say that, as regards the co-ordination of all ordinary properties of matter, Rutherford's model of the atom puts before us a task reminiscent of the old dream of philosophers: to reduce the interpretation of the laws of nature to the consideration of pure numbers."

It was in such an atmosphere, charged with the excitement of new discoveries and in anticipation of more fundamental and unifying ones to come, that Bohr proposed his famous theory of the hydrogen atom.

The work of Rutherford and Bohr gave us the picture of the elementary particles shown in Figure 5. The abscissa is the electric charge and the ordinate represents schematically, not to scale, the masses of the particles. The pro-

FIGURE 5

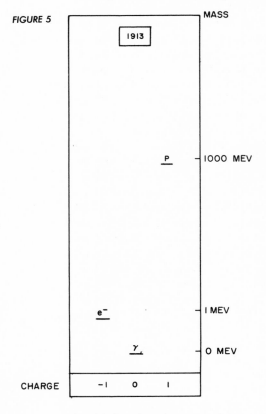

(Mass labeling schematic, not to scale.)

ton p is the hydrogen nucleus and the massless photon denoted by γ represents the quantum of the electromagnetic radiation. It had a distinguished history of its own. Max Planck, in his study of the theory of black body radiation, had found an empirical formula that fitted the experiments. The formula was however in contradiction to the classical concepts of electromagnetic radiation. To explain the formula, he made in 1901 the bold assumption that electromagnetic radiation cannot be emitted or absorbed except in certain units, or quanta, each quantum having an energy $h\nu$ where ν is the frequency of the radiation and h a universal constant introduced by Planck and later named after him. This atomic concept of the energy transfer between matter and the radiation field was so revolutionary it could only have originated from the thoroughness and the persistence that characterized Planck's studies. The concept was taken up, discussed, and molded by Albert Einstein in 1905 and greatly influenced Bohr in formulating his theory of the atom.

During the years following 1913, Herculean efforts were made to gain a more complete understanding of the quantum concept, especially through Bohr's correspondence principle, and to correlate the chemical properties of atoms with their quantum structure. To those of us who were educated after light and reason had struck in the final formulation of quantum mechanics, the subtle problems and the adventurous atmosphere of these pre-quantum mechanics days, at once full of promise and despair, seem to take on an almost eerie quality. We could only wonder what it was like when to reach correct conclusions through reasonings that were manifestly inconsistent constituted the art of the profession.

The climax was reached, as we all know, in the development of quantum mechanics in the years 1924–1927. The history of the intense drama of those few years remains to be written. Let me here only quote the beautifully eloquent description of J. R. Oppenheimer in his Reith Lectures of 1953, published as a small volume,[5] *Science and the Common Understanding:*

"Our understanding of atomic physics, of what we call the quantum theory of atomic systems, had its origins at the turn of the century and its great synthesis and resolutions in the nineteen-twenties. It was a heroic time. It was not the doing of any one man; it involved the collaboration of scores of scientists from many different lands, though from first to last the deeply creative and subtle and critical spirit of Niels Bohr guided, restrained, deepened, and finally transmuted the enterprise. It was a period of patient work in the laboratory, of crucial experiments and daring action, of many false starts and many untenable conjectures. It was a time of earnest correspondence and hurried conferences, of debate, criticism, and brilliant mathematical improvisation.

"For those who participated, it was a time of creation; there was terror as well as exaltation in their new insight. It will probably not be recorded very completely as history. As history, its recreation would call for an art as high as the story of Oedipus or the story of Cromwell, yet in a realm of action so remote from our common experience that it is unlikely to be known to any poet or any historian."

It is impossible to give here a description of the principles of quantum mechanics that is even remotely adequate. However, for the purpose of understanding our later discussions, one particular aspect of quantum mechanics must be introduced. We recall that Planck, Einstein, and Bohr had initiated the idea of the quantum concept of the radiation field which classically was well known to be waves. This particle aspect of the waves was confirmed by R. A. Millikan's experiments in 1916 on photoelectricity and again in 1923 by A. H. Compton who discovered that in collisions with electrons, X-rays, which are electromagnetic waves, behave exactly like particles in the transfer of momentum and energy. These particles that represent the X-ray are called photons and in Figure 5 were denoted by γ. The wave length λ and the momentum p of a photon were experimentally found to satisfy the condition that their product is equal to the Planck's constant h. Then in a paper in 1924, L. de Broglie raised the question that if waves show corpuscular character, should not particles also show wave character? He assumed that they should and that the waves associated with a particle have a wave length given by h divided by its momentum, just as in the case of a photon. This most daring assumption led him to the following picture of an electron in an orbit illustrated in Figure 6. He argued that if the orbit does not contain an integral number of wave lengths, as in the drawing on the left, the waves cannot resonate. In the drawing on the right, however, resonance occurs, and therefore the orbit represents an allowed orbit. In this way de Broglie actually arrived at Bohr's quantum condition of 1913 in a very suggestive way, a way that was explored by E. Schrödinger in 1926, leading to the famous Schrödinger's equation which formed one of the cornerstones of quantum mechanics.

FIGURE 6

Thus in quantum mechanics a particle shows wave characteristics with a wave length that is inversely proportional to its momentum. Now it is common knowledge that to localize a wave in a small region of space, wave lengths smaller than the dimensions of the region must be used. Thus to explore smaller and smaller regions of space one must use particles of higher and higher momentum so that the associated wave lengths could be small enough to fit into the region of space explored. This situation is illustrated in the following table which explains the reason why bigger and more energetic atom smashers are built. We shall have occasion to return to this subject later on.

TABLE 1

Distance		Momentum $\times$ c
10^{-8} cm		.002 Million volts (atomic phenomena)
10^{-12} cm	20	Million volts (nuclear phenomena)
10^{-14} cm	2,000	Million volts ($\sim$ present limit)
10^{-16} cm	200,000	Million volts (future ?)

We have previously quoted from Niels Bohr's Faraday Lecture in 1930. He described the important conceptual separation of atomic and molecular phenomena from nuclear phenomena as a result of Rutherford's picture of the atom. With the development of quantum mechanics, the understanding of atomic and molecular phenomena attained a level that is quantitative, complete, and profound—an understanding that is undoubtedly one of the greatest intellectual triumphs of all times. However a similar understanding of the nucleus was lacking, as it still is today. In many senses, the years around 1930 were very much like those around 1900, the latter representing the dawn of the era of atomic physics, the former, that of the era of nuclear physics.

FIGURE 7

To Pump

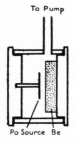

Po Source Be

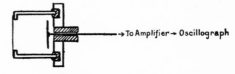

→ To Amplifier → Oscillograph

The first elementary particle discovered in this new era was the neutron. Curie-Joliot and Joliot had discovered in 1932 that, in an arrangement like that shown in Figure 7, the beryllium under the bombardment of the α particles from the polonium source emitted some very penetrating electrically neutral particles, which they found could knock out protons from hydrogen-containing material placed in front of the counter at the left. It was natural to assume that the neutral particles were photons. However, due to its lack of mass, it would have taken a photon of tremendous energy to knock out the protons observed. In fact, they concluded that the photon would have to have an energy of more than 50 Mev,[6] a very high energy in those days. As soon as these results were made known, J. Chadwick in Cambridge, England took up the experiment and showed that the penetrating particles were not massless, but had approximately the mass of the proton. Such a neutral particle had actually been discussed by Rutherford in 1920 and was called by him the neutron. In the 'twenties many experiments had been performed to search for it, but in vain.

With the discovery of the neutron it was immediately evident that atomic nuclei are made up of neutrons and protons in almost equal numbers. More accurate measurements of the neutron mass showed that it was quite a bit larger than that of the proton. It was later realized that the neutron should therefore be unstable and should disintegrate into an electron and a proton, in the fashion of beta radioactivity, a phenomenon known since about 1900. Experiments of beta disintegration in general showed, however, that to preserve energy conservation a new kind of neutral particle was needed to carry away the excess energy. This new kind of particle was called the neutrino by Enrico Fermi, and the decay process of the neutron came to be understood as

$$n \rightarrow p + e^- + \nu$$

where n and ν represent the neutron and the neutrino.

In the two years 1932–1933 another new particle, the positron, was discovered. This discovery was made possible through the use of an extremely ingenius instrument called the cloud chamber, invented and perfected by C. T. R. Wilson. Wilson described the origin of the cloud chamber thus:[7]

"In September 1894 I spent a few weeks in the observatory which then existed on the summit of Ben Nevis, the highest of the Scottish hills. The wonderful optical phenomena

FIGURE 8

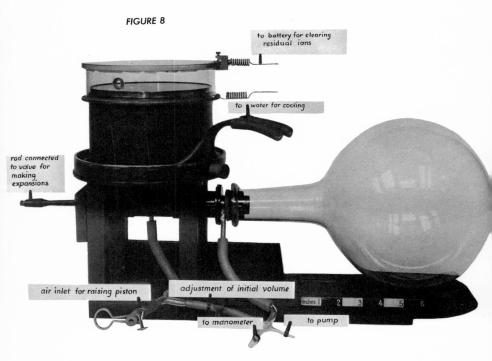

to battery for clearing residual ions

to water for cooling

rod connected to valve for making expansions

air inlet for raising piston

adjustment of initial volume

to manometer

to pump

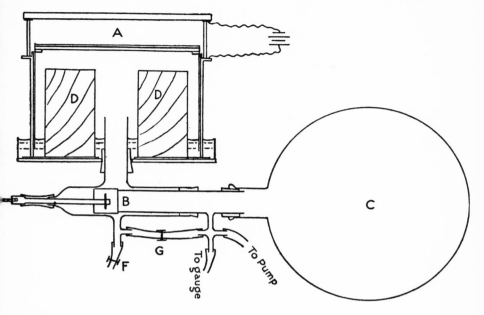

FIGURE 9

shown when the sun shone on the clouds surrounding the hill top, and especially the
coloured rings surrounding the sun or surrounding the shadow cast by the hill top or
observer on mist or cloud, greatly excited my
interest and made me wish to imitate them in
the laboratory.

At the beginning of 1895 I made some experiments for this purpose—making clouds by
expansion of moist air after the manner of
Coulier and Aitken. Almost immediately I
came across something which promised to be
of more interest than the optical phenomena
which I had intended to study."

This "something" led to the cloud chamber
in which charged particles leave a visible track
of water droplets in moist air, made supersat-
urated through sudden expansion. Figures 8
and 9 show the cloud chamber with which
Wilson took many beautiful photographs. It

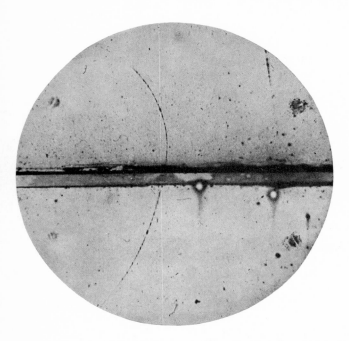

FIGURE 10 was with a similar cloud chamber that, in 1932, C .D. Anderson of the California Institute of Technology took the picture reproduced in Figure 10. A charged particle came in from the bottom and followed a circular path because of a strong magnetic field that was present in the chamber. It was slowed down in transversing the 6 millimeter lead plate and therefore came out with a much larger curvature. This fact that the upper part of the path has the larger curvature instead of the lower part proves that the particle must have been moving from the bottom to the top. Knowing the direction of motion, Anderson was then able to deduce that its charge was positive. Furthermore, from the magnitude of the change in the curvature in crossing the lead plate he was able to show conclusively that the particle was much lighter than a proton. Anderson concluded that the particle in fact had the mass of the electron and called it the positron.

The existence of the positron was actually theoretically predicted already during the years 1930–1931. The prediction was based on the beautiful theory of the electron formulated by P. A. M. Dirac which had led to the so-called principle of invariance under charge conjugation. One consequence of this principle was that to every particle there should exist a charge conjugate particle, or antiparticle, bearing the same mass and equal but opposite charge. The positron discovered by Anderson was the antiparticle of the electron.

In the year 1933 the number of elementary particles known had thus greatly increased, as is indicated in Figure 11. The e^- and e^+ are the electron and positron. The neutrino ν and the antineutrino $\bar{\nu}$ are charge conjugate particles of each other. In the course of the gradual unfolding of the properties of a particle, conventions have sometimes changed by accident or by intention, and the accepted convention today for the neutrino happens to be different from the one first discussed by Fermi. We now call the neutral particle emitted in neutron decay the antineutrino:

$$n \rightarrow p + e^- + \bar{\nu}.$$

The antiparticle of the photon γ is itself. At the bottom of the figure, underneath the charges, the intrinsic angular momenta or the spins of the particles are shown. These are in units of the Planck's constant divided by 2π. That angular momenta expressed in this unit should be multiples of one-half is a direct prediction of the principles of quantum mechanics, and is found to be in excellent agreement with experiments.

FIGURE 11, see next page

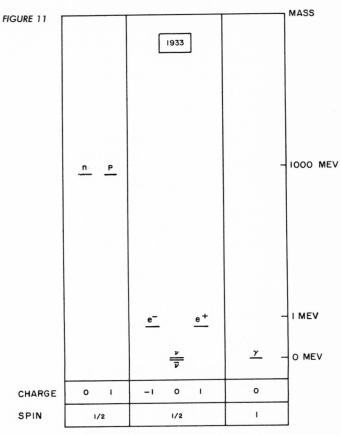

FIGURE 11

1933

MASS

n. P ──── 1000 MEV

e⁻   e⁺ ──── I MEV

$\frac{\nu}{\bar\nu}$ γ ──── O MEV

CHARGE	O I	−I O I	O
SPIN	1/2	1/2	I

(Mass labeling schematic, not to scale.)

Unstable particles are identified by wavy lines.

THE STORY of the discovery of the next elementary particle is long and involved. It started in 1935 with a suggestion of H. Yukawa that the protons and the neutrons in a nucleus are bound together through a mediating field in much the same way that the nucleus and the electron are bound in an atom through the intermediary of the electromagnetic field. Yukawa pointed out that the small size of the nucleus implies the shortness of the range of nuclear forces, which in turn, as we discussed in the previous lecture, is related to a large momentum carried by the field. Now by the principles of special relativity, the average momentum carried by the field is of the order of the velocity of light multiplied by the mass of the quantum that is associated with the field. From the size of nuclei, Yukawa thus estimated this mass to be approximately 200 times the electron mass. He then remarked,[8] "As such a quantum with large mass has never been found by experiment, the above theory seems to be on a wrong line." Yukawa did not know that at that very time C. D. Anderson and S. H. Neddermeyer were making extensive studies of the ability of the charged particles in the cosmic rays to penetrate matter. The studies were very difficult because it took a long time to gather enough experimental data. More than this, the experiments were difficult because the phenomena observed in cosmic rays were totally new to the physicists—the proper orientation and framework in which to approach the phenomena were not yet firmly established. When strange and unexpected things occurred, as they did, it was not clear whether new particles and/or new principles were involved, or whether the old particles and old principles were manifesting new surprising

2

behavior in a new domain of investigation. Anderson and Neddermeyer persisted in the face of these difficulties and through very careful studies in the years 1934, 1935, and 1936 came to the conclusion that new kinds of charged particles, some with positive and some negative charges, were present in the cosmic rays. These particles had a mass intermediate between the masses of the electron and the proton, and it was natural to conclude that they were the particles, predicted to exist by Yukawa, which serve to transmit the nuclear forces. They were at first called mesotrons, but later mesons. This discovery caused quite a stir among the psysicists, as is evident from the following passage in a letter[9] from Niels Bohr to Millikan in 1938:

"The story of the discovery of these particles is certainly a most wonderful one and the cautiousness for which I gave expression during the discussions in the unforgettable days in the spring before last in Pasadena was only dictated from the appreciation of the great consequences of Anderson's work, if the evidence for the new particles was really convincing. At the moment I do not know whether one shall admire most the ingenuity and foresight of Yukawa or the tenaciousness with which the group in your Institute kept on in tracing the indications of the new effects."

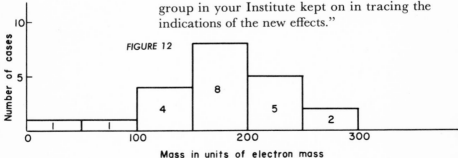

FIGURE 12

The birth pains of these new particles were, however, not yet over, for various measurements of the mass of the mesons yielded quite different results. The situation is illustrated in Figure 12, which is a compilation of the published experimental values up to 1945 of the meson mass in units of m_e, the mass of the electron. The average value was $172m_e$, but deviations from this average value were large. Extensive efforts were spent on more accurate measurements of the mass, and on more careful theoretical analysis of the data, but the first definitive indication that something more complex was in store came from the work of M. Conversi, E. Pancini, and O. Piccioni in their study of the interaction between the cosmic ray mesons and atomic nuclei. Their experiment, published in 1947, showed this interaction to be extremely weak. It was then emphasized by E. Fermi, E. Teller, and V. F. Weisskopf that something was terribly amiss, since these particles, which interact so little with nuclei, could not possibly serve to transmit the very strong nuclear forces. In fact they demonstrated that the cosmic ray mesons could only serve as the intermediary of forces weaker than the nuclear forces by a factor of at least 10^{13}. This large discrepancy led to very interesting theoretical speculations. In particular, S. Sakata and T. Inoue, and H. A. Bethe and R. E. Marshak, proposed that the cosmic ray mesons so far observed were *not* Yukawa's mesons. These latter also should exist in the cosmic rays, but did not live long enough to be observed by the then existing equipment. The final resolution of the problem came about in the following way.

Around that time C. F. Powell and his group in Bristol had developed the technique of using photographic emulsions to detect charged par-

FIGURE 13

ticles. The ions produced in the emulsions by the charged particles along their paths cause black grains to appear after development. These grains mark the tracks or paths of charged particles through the emulsion. Powell and his collaborators examined the tracks left by some of the charged particles of the cosmic rays in the photographic plate. Figure 13 shows some of these tracks in two mosaic views under microscopes. We observe that in each case among the background of random grains there are two clearly visible long wavy tracks. From the rate of change of the grain density along a track, and from the deviations of a track from a straight line due to the scattering of the particle in traversing the emulsions, it is possible to obtain a lot of information about the particle. For example, as a particle slows down, it ionizes more and therefore the grains along its track thicken. For the mosaic at the left, the interpretation is therefore that a particle came in near the bottom from the left, slowed down and stopped near the right bottom corner, disintegrated into some neutral particles which left no tracks and a charged particle which went upwards, slowed down and went out of the region covered by the mosaic. The other mosaic shows a very similar example. These two particular cases were actually the first two published by Powell's group of stopped mesons that gave rise to a secondary meson track. They named the primary and the secondary mesons π and μ mesons, as indicated in the figure. Later, a more sensitive photographic emulsion became available and it was found that a μ meson, if stopped in the emulsion, gave rise to a very light track which was identified as that left by an electron, as illustrated in Figure 14. The whole process was thus identified:

$$\pi^+ \rightarrow \mu^+ + \nu,$$
$$\mu^+ \rightarrow e^+ + \nu + \overline{\nu}.$$

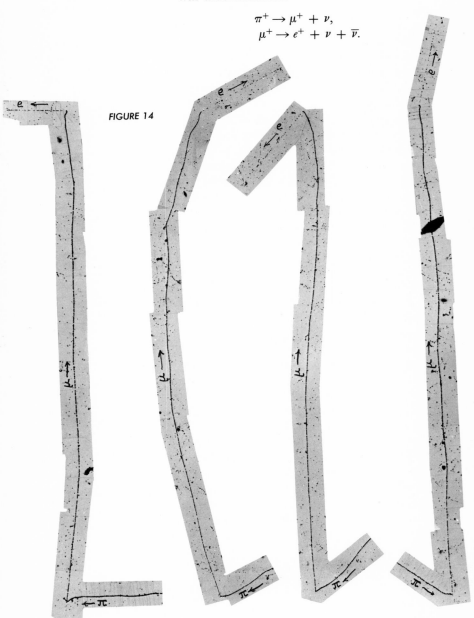

FIGURE 14

The neutrinos and antineutrinos, being neutral, do not leave visible tracks. Their place in these disintegrations were inferred from detailed studies of the energy, momentum and angular momentum balances in these disintegrations. The negatively charged π and μ mesons disintegrate in similar ways. The masses of the π and μ mesons were also obtained from these detailed studies. They are, respectively, 273 and 207 times the mass of the electron.

The discovery of the existence of two kinds of mesons eliminated the discrepancy mentioned earlier. The π meson is identified with Yukawa's meson, and serves as the intermediary for nuclear forces, while its daughter, the μ meson, is the cosmic ray meson observed by Conversi, Pancini, and Piccioni which does not interact strongly with atomic nuclei.

The beautiful and timely work of Powell's group, revealing this unexpected hierarchy of mesons, is another illustration of a fact we had mentioned before, that advances in our knowledge in physics are facilitated, and oftentimes only made possible, by the development and improvement of experimental techniques.

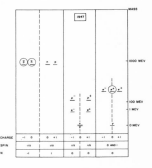

So we were led in 1947 to the following picture of the elementary particles (Figure 15). The new entries in this diagram are the π^+, π^-, μ^+, μ^- mesons. We also introduce circles around those particles whose existence was theoretically predicted but whose experimental discovery was yet to be made. In this category there were the electrically neutral π^0 meson, the antiproton $\bar{p}$ and the antineutron $\bar{n}$. The concept of charge conjugation symmetry, which had taken root at that time, is indicated through vertical dotted lines. Within each of the three vertical columns, the particles and their corre-

FIGURE 15, see next page

sponding antiparticles form mirror images with respect to the dotted line. The π^0 and the γ-ray are their own antiparticles. You will notice that we introduce here a new row labelled by N at the bottom of the diagram. The meaning of this number is explainable as follows: most particles in this diagram have a tendency to disintegrate into lighter ones. For example, the π mesons are unstable, the μ mesons are unstable, and also the neutron n and its antiparticle $\bar{n}$ are unstable. Their disintegration schemes have been previously discussed.[10] However, from the stability of the hydrogen nucleus it is evident that the proton p does not disintegrate. The unstable particles are indicated in the diagram by wavy lines. The stable particles are, beside the proton p, the electron e^-, the positron e^+, the neutrino ν, the antineutrino $\bar{\nu}$, and the photon γ. Now the stability of the last three particles is easy to understand: mass, as is well known, is equivalent to energy. To conserve energy, a particle can only disintegrate into particles *lighter* than itself, the balance of the mass being made up by the kinetic energies of the disintegration products. The neutrino ν, the antineutrino $\bar{\nu}$ and the photon γ are massless. With no particles lighter than they, there are no particles for them to decay into. There is also a simple reason for the stability of $e^{\pm}$: they are the lightest charged particles. Since charge is not increased or decreased in a disintegration, they are stuck with their charges and cannot disintegrate. We are thus left with the stability of the proton p and the antiproton $\bar{p}$ unaccounted for. For example, why does a proton not decay into a positron and a photon:

$$p \rightarrow e^+ + \gamma \, ?$$

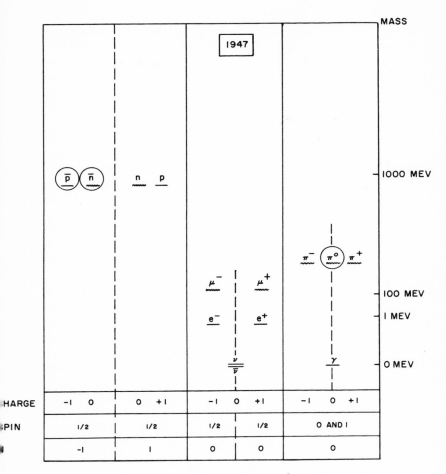

An answer to this question has not yet been found. To phenomenologically describe this stability, however, physicists assign to each particle a number N, in analogy with the electric charge. The total value of N of a collection of particles is, by this assignment, the total number of protons p and neutrons n minus the total number of $\bar{p}$ and $\bar{n}$. One then proposes that in a reaction or disintegration, N is con-

FIGURE 15

(Mass labeling schematic, not to scale.) Unstable particles are identified by wavy lines. Encircled particles are those theoretically predicted to exist but not yet experimentally found at this date.

27

served, just as the electric charge is conserved. In fact N is called the "Nucleon Charge." The stability of p and $\bar{p}$ is then entirely similar to that of $e^{\pm}$: p and $\bar{p}$ are the lightest particles with non-vanishing nucleon charge. They are stuck with their nucleon charges and cannot disintegrate.

The situation as existed in 1947 and represented in Fig. 15 constituted a not too complicated picture. The neutrons, protons, electrons and photons were familiar objects. The π meson had its "reason" for existence as the intermediary through which nuclear forces were transmitted. Together with the concept of the existence of antiparticles, the only elementary particles unbargained for in this picture were the μ mesons and the neutrinos.

This relatively simple state of affairs did not, however, last very long. In fact right in 1947, from a large number of cloud chamber photographs of cosmic ray penetrating shower particles, G. D. Rochester and C. C. Butler in Manchester obtained the two photographs shown schematically in Figure 16. In the picture at the left they identified the tracks a and b as due to the charged disintegration products of a neutral particle of mass around 1,000 electron masses, which was different from the masses of all previously known particles. They also obtained the picture on the right in which

FIGURE 16

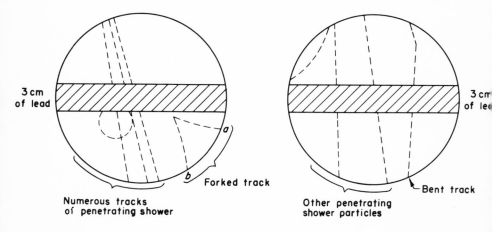

3 cm of lead

3 cm of lead

a)

b

Forked track

Bent track

Numerous tracks of penetrating shower

Other penetrating shower particles

they concluded the bent track represented the disintegration of a charged particle of mass around 1,000 electron masses into a neutral and a secondary charged particle. Two years later, in 1949, using the new photographic emulsion technique, Powell and his collaborators obtained the following picture of a cosmic ray particle (Figure 17). They identified it as a particle k coming to a stop at the point A and disintegrating into three π mesons, Aa, Ab, and AB. The last of these caused a nuclear disintegration at B. Both the disintegration scheme and the mass of the primary particle k did not fit with any of the known particles at that time. Powell and his group called this newly discovered particle a τ meson.

These three pictures gave us the first glimpse into the totally unexpected and complex pattern of many new particles. Because they were unexpected, they were given the collective name of "strange particles" They are produced in collisions in which energies of more than one billion electron volts are involved. In the years 1948–1953 the only available source of such high energies was from cosmic rays. Accordingly many investigations were launched to study the existence of strange new particles in cosmic rays. The cosmic rays are, however, not a controllable source of high energy particles. And the frequency of occurrence of high energy cosmic ray particles in an instrument of any reasonable size was very small. Thanks to the rapid development of the technology and the art of constructing high energy machines, it fortunately became feasible around that time to construct machines in the billion electron volt range. When the first such machine, called the cosmotron, went into operation in 1953 at the Brookhaven National

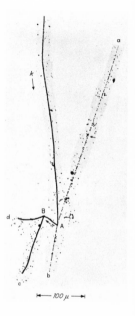

FIGURE 17, see next page

29

FIGURE 17

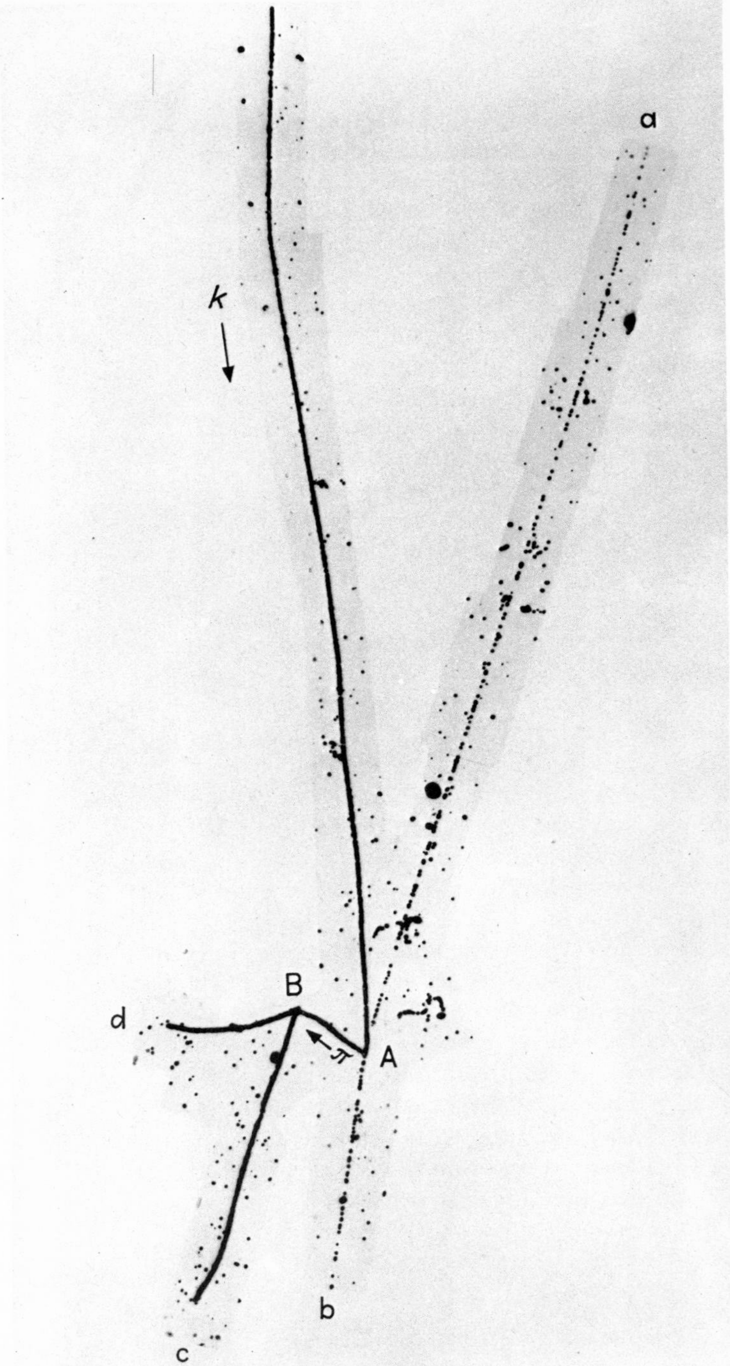

Laboratory on Long Island, it became possible to have strange particles produced to order in the laboratory.

The list of particles that were identified, named, and studied by the combined use of cosmic ray and machine-produced events, added to those previously known, now number thirty. They are represented in Figure 18.

FIGURE 18

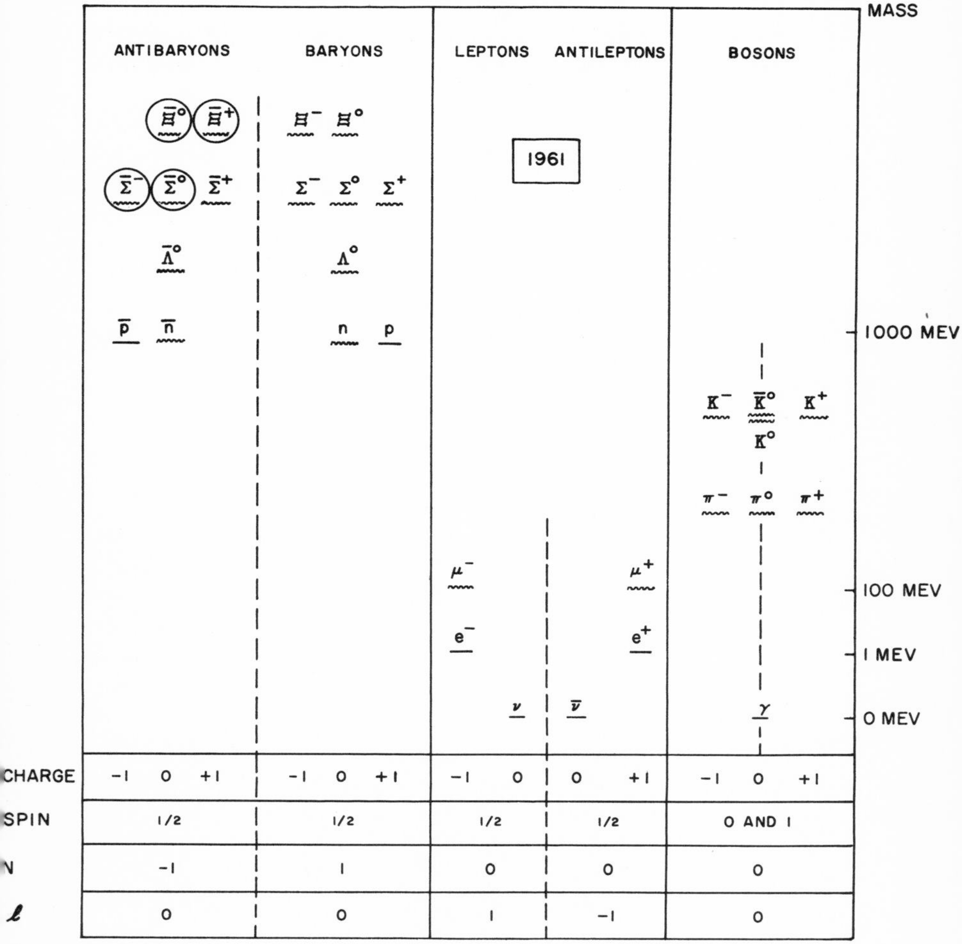

MASS

| ANTIBARYONS | BARYONS | LEPTONS | ANTILEPTONS | BOSONS |

1961

$\overline{\Xi}^{\circ}$ $\overline{\Xi}^{+}$ Ξ^{-} Ξ°

$\overline{\Sigma}^{-}$ $\overline{\Sigma}^{\circ}$ $\overline{\Sigma}^{+}$ Σ^{-} Σ° Σ^{+}

$\overline{\Lambda}^{\circ}$ Λ°

$\overline{p}$ $\overline{n}$ n p — 1000 MEV

K^{-} $\overline{K}^{\circ}$ K^{+}
K°

π^{-} π° π^{+}

μ^{-} μ^{+} — 100 MEV

e^{-} e^{+} — 1 MEV

ν $\overline{\nu}$ γ — 0 MEV

	ANTIBARYONS	BARYONS	LEPTONS	ANTILEPTONS	BOSONS
CHARGE	−1 0 +1	−1 0 +1	−1 0	0 +1	−1 0 +1
SPIN	1/2	1/2	1/2	1/2	0 AND 1
N	−1	1	0	0	0
ℓ	0	0	1	−1	0

(Mass labeling schematic, not to scale.) Unstable particles are identified by wavy lines. Encircled particles are those theoretically predicted to exist but not yet experimentally found at this date.

There are three major families of particles; baryons and antibaryons form the first family, leptons and antileptons the second, and bosons the third. Within each family, particles and antiparticles occupy mirror image positions with respect to the vertical dotted lines. The ordinate is the mass of the particle, the base line for zero mass being at the level of the ν, $\bar{\nu}$, and γ. The abcissa within each block is the electric charge of the particle. The encircled particles are those still not experimentally found, but which are predicted to exist.

A new row labeled l is introduced in this diagram. It represents a concept developed in the last ten years, and is called the lepton number. In a reaction or decay the total value of l is conserved, just as the total electric charge, and the total nucleon charge N are both conserved. As an illustration of an example of l conservation, we can take the case of neutron decay

$$n \rightarrow p + e^- + \bar{\nu}$$

in which $l = 0$ both before and after the decay process.

For an example of a rather spectacular event, let us look at Figure 19 which is a picture of a hydrogen-filled bubble chamber through which antiprotons $\bar{p}$ traverse from the bottom up. The principle of the bubble chamber will be discussed later. For the purpose here we need only say that it closely resembles a cloud chamber. The interpretation of the picture is based on curvature measurements on the tracks which allow for a quantitative check of energy and momentum balance. The interpretation is given in the upper right corner. In it we see the following events:

at A, $\bar{p} + p \rightarrow \Lambda^0 + \bar{\Lambda}^0$,   (collision of $\bar{p}$ with a hydrogen nucleus in the chamber);

at B, $\Lambda^0 \rightarrow \pi^- + p$,   (decay);

at C, $\bar{\Lambda}^0 \rightarrow \pi^+ + \bar{p}$,   (decay);

at D, $\bar{p} + p \rightarrow \pi^+ + \pi^+ + \pi^- + \pi^-$,   (collision of the $\bar{p}$ from $\bar{\Lambda}^0$ decay with a hydrogen nucleus in the chamber).

It is simple to check in detail that in each of these reactions and decays, the total N, the total l, and the total electric charge are separately conserved.

FIGURE 19

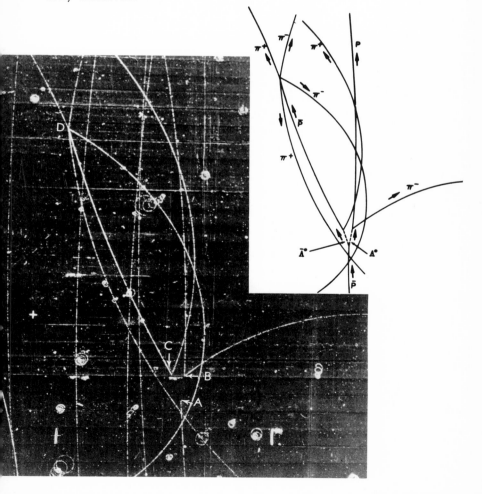

A word should be mentioned about the names of the elementary particles. When a particle was first found it was usually under difficult circumstances and information about it was usually scanty. Names were given to designate them but it was common for several particles, later found to be different, to share the same name. It was also common for the same particle to have several different names because it appeared in different forms in different experiments. A considerable amount of work in the study of the particles consisted in tracking them down, giving them names and, so to speak, cataloging them. The names in Figure 18 are the now accepted names. The τ meson, discovered by Powell and his group in 1949, is now called the K meson. We shall have occasion to return to this particular point in the next lecture.

The names π meson and μ meson are oftentimes contracted into pions and muons. Recently one also finds the short name, kaon, for the K meson. One shudders at the prospect of reading about lambdaons and sigmaons.

Before we discuss the intricacies and puzzlement, the hopes and frustrations in the study of these particles in the last dozen years, a short discussion of experimental facilities is perhaps in order: first, about the production of the particles by high energy machines. Developments of these machines began in the same years (1932–1933) when interest in the study of nuclear physics was starting to gather momentum. It is indeed amazing that within those two years the first Van de Graaff accelerator, the first Cockcroft-Walton accelerator, and the first cyclotron were all taking shape. These were ingenious though modest devices for accelerating particles to several million volts. They opened the way to the principles of the construction of the giant machines of today.

It has already been pointed out that high energy machines are necessary to study small distances. It may be asked why it is that a high energy machine has to be physically big in size. The answer is simple: To accelerate a particle to higher and higher energies one has to "push" it for longer and longer periods of time. During these longer periods of time the particle travels longer distances. If one tries to confine these longer distances into a small region of space by an arrangement such that the particles remain in a "race track" while being accelerated, the race track has to be large since it is difficult to bend the trajectory of a high energy particle. Furthermore the rigidity of the trajectory increases with increasing energy of the particle, making it necessary to have physically larger and larger machines as one attempts to study smaller and smaller distances.

In Figure 20 is shown a view of the Brookhaven National Laboratory cosmotron that can accelerate particles to 3 billion electron volts.

FIGURE 20

Protons are injected into the ring shaped machine from the horizontal cylindrical Van de Graaff accelerator in the middle part of the figure, behind the machine. They are kept racing around in the machine for about one second, receiving periodically forward pushes which accelerate them to three billion volts. They are then made to strike a target in the machine. The products of the collision are either made to strike secondary targets, or are directly studied with various types of detectors.

Figure 21 is an aerial view of the 30 billion volt machine also at the Brookhaven laboratory. The picture was taken several years ago, showing the excavation for the big race track with the injection station at the six o'clock position, and the experimental area at the twelve o'clock position. The machine was completed in the summer of 1960. An almost identical machine was put into operation half a year earlier in Geneva, Switzerland. Besides these machines, there are currently three others in operation in the multibillion volt range: the

FIGURE 21 Bevatron of 6 billion volts at Berkeley, the

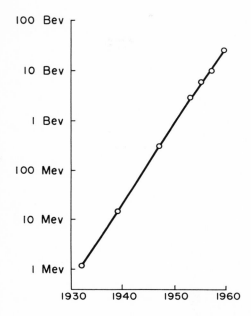

FIGURE 22

Dubna machine of 10 billion volts near Moscow, and the Saclay machine of 3 billion volts near Paris. A machine of about 3 billion volts with high intensity is under construction here in Princeton, and is due to be finished in a year or two.

As these machines become larger and larger, and more and more costly, one is inclined to ask where the end will be. Figure 22 shows a plot of the energy attained at various times in the past. How to extrapolate into the future is something all of us have yet to learn.

Let us next consider the detectors, which are instruments with which the phenomena produced by the high energy particles are recorded and analysed. Table 2 lists the three principle types of detectors in use. We have already seen what pictures taken with the photographic emulsion and with a cloud chamber look like. The antiproton and antilambda picture (Figure 19) was taken with a bubble chamber. Chadwick's instrument for the discovery of the neutron (Figure 7) included a counter which belongs to the first type of detectors.

TABLE 2

Three Types of Detectors of Charged Particles

I.   Ionization chamber, Geiger counter, Scintillation counter, Cerenkov counter, etc.

II.   Cloud chamber, Diffusion chamber, Bubble chamber.

III.   Photographic Emulsion.

There is constant progress in the development of new types of detectors and, as we have emphasized before, these advancements stimulate and make possible new discoveries and new

FIGURE 23

understanding of the elementary particles. It is unfortunate that like the accelerating machines, the detectors also these days have a tendency to become big and expensive. Figure 23, for example, shows the control room of a big bubble chamber at Berkeley. A comparison of this figure with, for example, the simple detector of Chadwick (Figure 7) is likely to fill one with a mixed feeling of admiration for the technological progress and skepticism for the future prospects of the rapid growth of the complexity and size of the equipments.

Big accelerators and big detectors of course need the attention of many workers. Consequently we have the pheonomena of multiple authorship of papers illustrated in Figure 24.

FIGURE 24

On the Masses and Modes of Decay of Heavy Mesons Produced by Cosmic Radiation.

(G-Stack Collaboration)

J. H. DAVIES, D. EVANS, P. E. FRANCOIS, M. W. FRIEDLANDER, R. HILLIER, P. IREDALE, D. KEEFE, M. G. K. MENON, D. H. PERKINS and C. F. POWELL

H. H. Wills Physical Laboratory - Bristol (Br)

J. BØGGILD, N. BRENE, P. H. FOWLER, J. HOOPER, W. C. G. ORTEL and M. SCHARFF

Institut för Teoretisk Fysik - København (Ko)

L. CRANE, R. H. W. JOHNSTON and C. O'CEALLAIGH

Institute for Advanced Studies - Dublin (DuAS)

F. ANDERSON, G. LAWLOR and T. E. NEVIN

University College - Dublin (DuUC)

G. ALVIAL, A. BONETTI, M. DI CORATO, C. DILWORTH, R. LEVI SETTI, A. MILONE (+), G. OCCHIALINI (*), L. SCARSI and G. TOMASINI (+)

(+) *Istituto di Fisica dell'Università - Genova*
Istituto di Scienze Fisiche dell'Università - Milano (GeMi)
Istituto Nazionale di Fisica Nucleare - Sezione di Milano
(*) *and of Laboratoire de Physique Nucléaire - Université Libre - Bruxelles*

M. CECCARELLI, M. GRILLI, M. MERLIN, G. SALANDIN and B. SECHI

Istituto di Fisica dell'Università - Padova
Istituto Nazionale di Fisica Nucleare - Sezione di Padova (Pd)

(ricevuto il 2 Ottobre 1955)

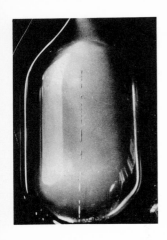

FIGURE 25

The necessary tendency toward bigness is unfortunate, as it hinders free and individual initiative. It makes research less intimate, less inspiring, and less controllable. However, it must be accepted as a fact of life. Let us take courage then in the knowledge that despite their physical bigness, the machines, the detectors, and indeed the experiments themselves are still based on ideas that have the same simplicity, the same intimacy and controllability that have always made research so exciting and inspiring. A good illustration of this point is the bubble chamber itself, which has now attained a mammoth size that is only suggested by the complexity of the control room illustrated in Fig. 23. The principle of the bubble chamber is similar to that of Wilson's cloud chamber. A liquid is made superheated and ready to boil. Bubbles have a tendency to form where ionization takes place along the paths of charged particles. Figure 25 shows the original chamber in which such a track of a cosmic ray μ-meson consisting of a string of bubbles was first photographed by D. A. Glaser. The chamber was only a few centimeters long. Legend has it that Glaser first conceived of the idea of the chamber while watching bubbles grow from some rough points on the walls of a beer bottle. Should the legend prove untrue, it serves to illustrate our point just as well.

40

THE INVESTIGATIONS carried out in the various laboratories have produced interesting information concerning the elementary particles. We shall try to describe some of these at this point. In all fields of research, when one is struggling with problems which are not within one's previous domain of experience, the very definition of the problem is often obscure. To be able to forge ahead, ingenuity and technical proficiency are of course required. But more important, there must be above all an independence of judgment which can come only from confidence and solidarity in the old knowledge, and persistence and boldness in the quest into the new. This is not easy to achieve—we should not expect it to be. In an article commemorating the seventieth birthday of Einstein, Philipp Frank said he had spoken to Einstein one day about a certain physicist who had had very little success in his research work. He consistently attacked problems which offered tremendous difficulties. He applied penetrating analysis and succeeded only in discovering more and more difficulties; he was not rated very highly by most of his colleagues. Einstein, according to Frank, said, "I admire this type of man. I have little patience with scientists who take a board of wood, look for its thinnest part and drill a great number of holes where drilling is easy."

Of course it is true that most of the time persistence in a new field of research leads only to more difficulties, or to blind alleys. Let us, however, look at one of these blind alleys; namely, Thomson's idea of an atom, which today we can view with a detachment that comes with the benefit of sixty years of hindsight. We remember that upon the discovery of the electron, Thomson had the picture of

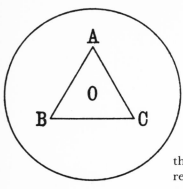

FIGURE 26

FIGURE 27

the atom shown in Figure 26. The electrons reside at positions of equilibrium, A, B, and C, around which they vibrate when disturbed. By measuring the amount of scattering of X-rays by various matter, he was led to a calculation of the number of electrons per atom in different chemical elements, and arrived at remarkably correct conclusions. Thomson saw that the electronic structure of the atoms offered the enormously important possibility of explaining the chemical properties of the elements. He then asked, what should be the structure of an atom with one electron, with two electrons, three electrons, etc.? The picture shown here represents that of three electrons embedded in a uniformly and positively charged sphere. For four electrons it is intuitively obvious that the positions of equilibrium for the electrons form the corners of a regular tetrahedron. However, when one considers atoms with more electrons, the mathematical problem of finding their equilibrium positions, though well defined, is difficult to solve. Thomson therefore had recourse to the following experimental arrangement to simulate mechanically the structure of his atom. By the use of corks, a number of long needle magnets were made to float in water in the manner shown in Figure 27. The poles of the needle magnets were made parallel to each other so that forces between them were repulsive, and in fact followed the inverse square law in the same way that the electrons in an atom repel each other. To artificially

produce the influence of the uniform positive charge in the atom which serves to hold the electrons in their equilibrium positions, he applied a magnetic field generated by an electromagnet high above the surface of the water. It is easy to demonstrate that the horizontal component of the magnetic force due to the electromagnet on any one of the needles, is approximately proportional to the distance from the needle to the point directly underneath the magnet. In Thomson's atom, the same is true of the force exerted by the uniform positive charge distribution on the electrons. The equilibrium configuration assumed by the floating magnetic needles is therefore an approximate solution of the electron configuration in Thomson's atom for the two-dimensional case. Figure 28 shows the configurations found by Thomson. One sees the interesting arrangement that for large numbers of needles, rings

FIGURE 28

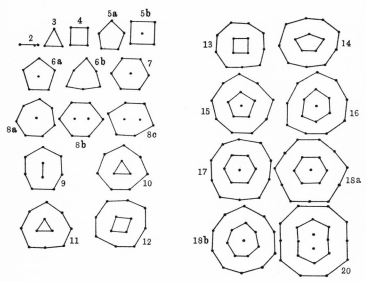

43

1.	2.	3.	4.	5.
1 . 5	2 . 6	3 . 7	4 . 8	5 . 9
1 . 6	2 . 7	3 . 8	4 . 9	—
1 . 7	—	—	—	—
1 . 5 . 9	2 . 7 . 10	3 . 7 . 10	4 . 8 . 12	5 . 9 . 12
1 . 6 . 9	2 . 8 . 10	3 . 7 . 11	4 . 8 . 13	5 . 9 . 13
1 . 6 . 10	2 . 7 . 11	3 . 8 . 10	4 . 9 . 12	—
1 . 6 . 11	—	3 . 8 . 11	4 . 9 . 13	—
—	—	3 . 8 . 12	—	—
—	—	3 . 8 . 13	—	—
1 . 5 . 9 . 12	2 . 7 . 10 . 15	3 . 7 . 12 . 13	4 . 9 . 13 . 14	—
1 . 5 . 9 . 13	2 . 7 . 12 . 14	3 . 7 . 12 . 14	4 . 9 . 13 . 15	—
1 . 6 . 9 . 12	—	3 . 7 . 13 . 14	4 . 9 . 14 . 15	—
1 . 6 . 10 . 12	—	3 . 7 . 13 . 15	—	—
1 . 6 . 10 . 13	—	—	—	—
1 . 6 . 11 . 12	—	—	—	—
1 . 6 . 11 . 13	—	—	—	—
1 . 6 . 11 . 14	—	—	—	—
1 . 6 . 11 . 15	—	—	—	—

FIGURE 29

are formed. In Figure 29 is shown a tabulation by Thomson of the number of needles in each ring. A comparison of this table with the periodic table then known, suggested itself. Thomson and his students were thus led to many investigations of such configurations and of the vibrational frequencies of the electrons embedded in the positions of equilibrium. We know today that these efforts were not along the right track. But we also know today that they were not in vain: as we have discussed previously, it was exactly out of such considerations that the eventually correct idea of Rutherford's atom grew.

Let us now try to describe in some detail four items from the study of the elementary particles in the last ten years. The first one concerns a puzzle presented by the experimental data around the years 1951–1952. It was found at that time that strange particles were produced quite copiously in collisions between high energy particles. Since the size, or extension of these particles is of the order of 10^{-13} centimeters, and since the velocity of approach between the particles is of the order of the velocity of light, namely 3×10^{10} centimeters per second, the collision time is obviously of the order of 10^{-23} seconds. This 10^{-23} seconds is therefore in many senses a unit of the time scale of these phenomena. It was also already known at that time that the strange particles are unstable, disintegrating into various kinds of particles. The average lifetime of each of these particles is measurable by many methods. For example, in Figure 30 is shown the production of a Λ at A. It is a neutral particle and therefore does not leave any visible track in the chamber, only betraying its existence when it disintegrates into a proton and a π^- at B. The distance between the birth and the death of the Λ is easily measured. The

FIGURE 30

velocity of the Λ can be inferred from the velocities of its disintegration products, which in turn are measurable by the curvatures of their tracks. From the distance AB and the velocity it is elementary to obtain the lifetime of this particular Λ. Taking the average of many such measurements, the mean lifetime of the Λ was determined to be a few times 10^{-10} seconds. This is a very short lifetime viewed from the human scale, but a tremendously long lifetime viewed from the time scale of 10^{-23} seconds mentioned above. In Table 4 at the end of the book the mean lifetimes and disintegration products of various particles are listed.

The strange particles are thus produced in times of the order of 10^{-23} seconds, and disintegrate in about 10^{-10} seconds, a time interval longer than the nuclear time scale by a factor of 10^{13}. In other words, the production process clearly involves forces stronger than the disintegration process by a factor of 10^{13}. Since both processes seemed to involve similar particles it was very puzzling why they took place with such drastically different rates, or strengths.

The resolution of this puzzle came with the suggestion of A. Pais and of Y. Nambu that the strange particles are *produced in groups* of more than one, in which situation they interact *strongly* with themselves and with the other particles involved in the process. On the other hand, in cases where they participate singly, as in the *disintegration* processes, they interact only *weakly*. This idea of the "associated production" process later received detailed experimental confirmation. The following picture (Figure 31) was one of the first observed associated productions of strange particles in the laboratory. It gives stereoscopic views of the following sequence of events: the incoming π^- meson leaving the track AB collided with a proton of the chamber at the point B, producing a K^0 meson and a Λ, both strange particles:

$$\pi^- + p \rightarrow K^0 + \Lambda \text{ (strong process).}$$

FIGURE 31

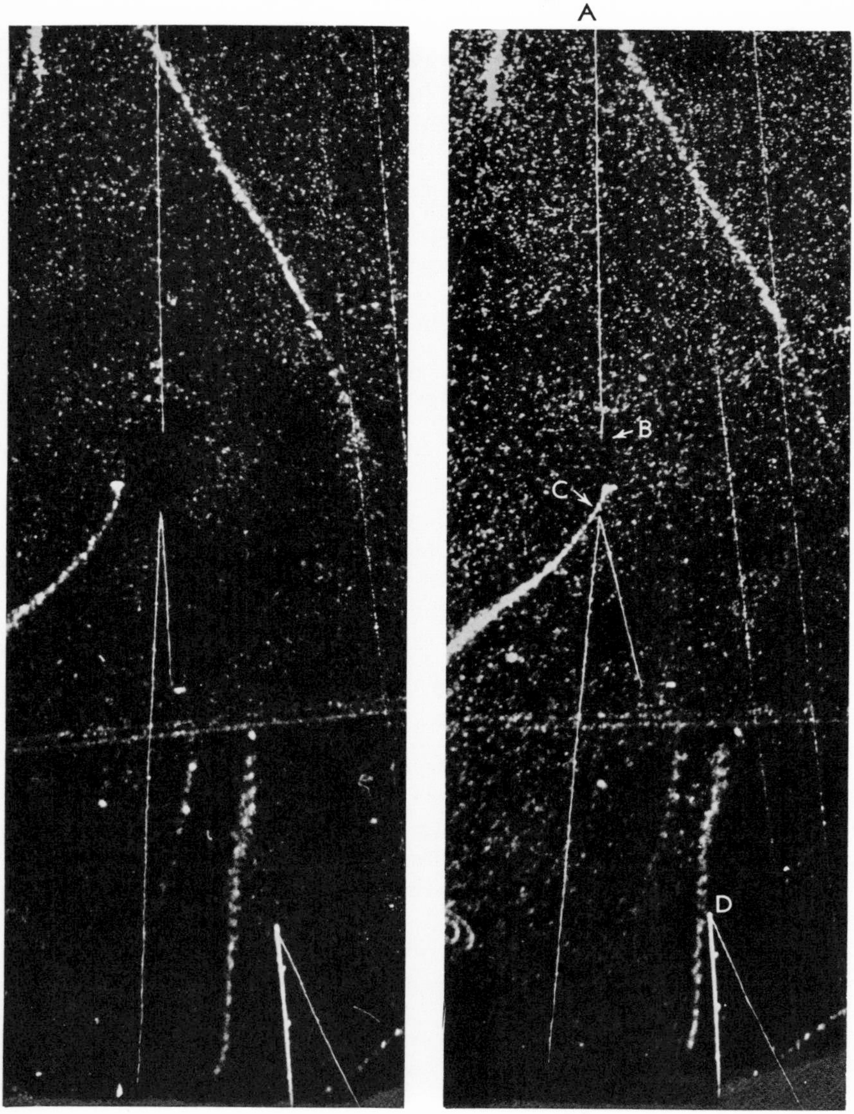

The K^0 and the Λ later disintegrated respectively at the points C and D:

$$K^0 \rightarrow \pi^+ + \pi^- \quad \text{(weak processs)},$$
$$\Lambda \rightarrow \pi^- + p \quad \text{(weak process)}.$$

We shall now come to the second item to be discussed: the classification of the strengths of interactions. We have already seen that an associated production of strange particles is caused by a strong interaction, and a disintegration of a strange particle by a weak interaction. Such a classification into strong and weak interactions was first discussed in the years 1948–1949 and is now known to be applicable to all measured interactions. The resulting picture is illustrated in the following table.

TABLE 3

	Strength
1. STRONG INTERACTIONS (Nuclear Interactions)	1
2. ELECTROMAGNETIC INTERACTIONS	10^{-2}
3. WEAK INTERACTIONS (Decay Interactions)	10^{-13}
4. GRAVITATIONAL INTERACTIONS	10^{-38}

In this table the strong interactions include those responsible for the associated production of strange particles, those representing the forces that bind the particles in a nucleus together, and also those responsible for various π meson interactions, such as

$$p + p \rightarrow \pi^+ + p + n.$$

The third category consists of the interactions responsible for the decays tabulated in Table 4. The ratio of the strengths of the first and the third categories is the factor 10^{13} mentioned before, and is indicated in the column labelled "strength." In describing the discovery of the $\pi \rightarrow \mu$ decay process we mentioned that prior to the discovery there was a large discrepancy of a factor 10^{13}. That was the same factor 10^{13} that separates the strong from the weak interactions: the π mesons interact with atomic nuclei through the strong interactions, while the μ mesons in the experiment of Conversi, Pancini, and Piccioni interact with the atomic nuclei through weak interactions.

The other two entries in Table 3 are more familiar interactions. The electromagnetic interactions, through the theories of Faraday and Maxwell, are the best understood of all. The gravitational interactions, though important when very heavy bodies such as the sun or the earth are involved, are extremely weak between the elementary particles, as indicated in the column labelled "strength." Because of this, gravitational interactions have so far fallen outside the range of elementary particle studies, though few physicists doubt that ultimately they must be brought in to give a unified picture.

Let us emphasize that the classification of interactions depicted here gives us one of the very important orientations in the study of elementary particles. It allows for a clear cut separation of the complex manifestations of each of the four types of interactions. The deep and difficult question of the origin of such a clear cut separation, and in particular, the origin of the approximate equality of the strengths of the many unrelated weak interactions remains unsolved.

The third item concerns a phenomenon called isotopic spin symmetry. Without explaining in detail what this symmetry means, let us look again at Figure 18 listing the elementary particles. One observes that the particles occur very remarkably in "multiplets" or groups with different charges but almost the same mass. The oldest known of these multiplets is the one consisting of the neutron and the proton. That the neutron and the proton are similar to each other, except for their electric charge, already suggested itself in the phenomenon that nuclei tend to have equal numbers of neutrons and protons. This was observed and discussed in the early 1930's, and received increasingly detailed experimental support as time went on. Among these was the observation that the newly discovered particles also occurred in multiplets. To find a deeper reason behind this symmetry is another very striking and tantalizing problem that has so far defied all efforts of investigation.

The phenomena of associated production and isotopic spin symmetry are related to each other, as was pointed out independently by M. Gell-Mann and K. Nishijima around 1953. They observed that the center of charge of a multiplet of strange particles may be displaced from that of the non-strange particles; for example, the Λ is displaced by half a unit of charge toward the left from the neutron-proton multiplet. A new quantity called the strangeness was introduced, with a value equal to twice the amount of this displacement. In Table 4 the strangenesses of the elementary particles are listed. It can be shown that isotopic spin symmetry implies that in a strong interaction the sum total of the strangenesses of the particles remains unchanged in the process. This rule is called the strangeness conservation rule. It has become one of the most fruitful concepts in the study of the strange particles. For example in the process

$$\pi^- + p \to \pi^0 + \Lambda$$

the sum total of the strangenesses of the particles before the process is (according to Table 4) 0. The sum total of the strangenesses of the particles after the process is -1. According to the rule this process is not strong, a conclusion in agreement with experiments. On the other hand, the process

$$\pi^- + p \to K^0 + \Lambda,$$

a picture of which we have seen in Fig. 31, conserves strangeness. The rule predicts that this process is strong, again in agreement with experimental results.

The fourth item we shall discuss concerns the symmetry principles, of which the isotopic spin symmetry discussed above is a special kind. The word symmetry is a common word used in daily language. Hermann Weyl in his Vanuxem Lectures of 1951 gave a beautiful exposition of the subject of symmetry in the arts, in nature, and in mathematics. The following two figures are examples of man-made and natural symmetries taken from illustrations in a book, *Symmetry,* which reproduces his lectures. In Figure 32 is shown an example of a lattice structure for a Chinese window. In

FIGURE 32

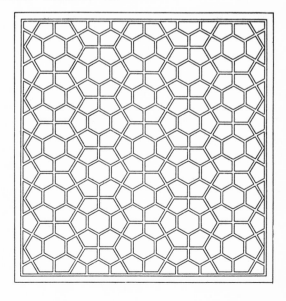

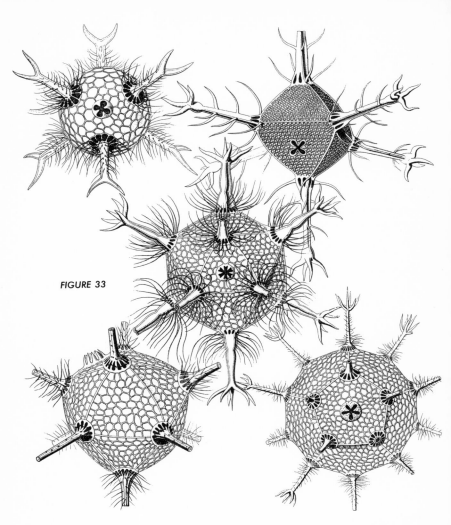

FIGURE 33

Figure 33 are examples of symmetries from the realm of living organisms.

The concept of symmetry in physics stems directly from our everyday notion. By tracing symmetries in a dynamical problem important conclusions can be reached. For example, a circular orbit of an electron in a hydrogen atom is a consequence and an indication of the symmetry of the Coulomb force exerted by the nucleus on the electron. The symmetry in this case means that the force has the same magnitude in all directions. Symmetry principles like this have played a role in classical physics, but in quantum mechanics the role has greatly gained both in depth and breadth. For example, the elliptical orbits as well as the circular orbits now assume a role in symmetry considerations. Indeed it is scarcely possible to over-emphasize the importance of the symmetry principles in quantum mechanics. To give two examples: the general structure of the periodic table is essentially a direct and beautiful consequence of the symmetry referred to above, the isotropy of the Coulomb force; the existence of the antiparticles, as we discussed before, were anticipated in Dirac's theory, which was built on the principle of relativistic symmetry. In both cases, as in other examples, nature seems to take advantage of the simple mathematical representation of the symmetry laws. The intrinsic elegance and beautiful perfection of the mathematical reasoning involved and the complexity and depth of the physical consequences are great sources of encouragement to physicists. One learns to hope that nature possesses an order that one may aspire to comprehend.

One of the symmetry principles, the symmetry between the left and the right, has been discussed since ancient times. The question whether nature exhibits such symmetry was debated at great length by philosophers of the past. In daily life, of course, right and left are quite different from each other. In biological phenomena, it was known since Pasteur's work in 1848 that organic compounds appear oftentimes in the form of only one of two kinds, both of which, however, occur in inorganic

53

processes and are mirror images of each other. In fact, Pasteur had considered for a time the idea that the ability to produce only one of the two forms was the very prerogative of life.[11]

The laws of physics, however, have always shown complete symmetry between the left and the right. This symmetry can also be formulated in quantum mechanics as a conservation law called the conservation of parity, which is completely identical to the principle of right-left symmetry. The first formulation of the concept of parity was due to E. P. Wigner. It rapidly became very useful in the analysis of atomic spectra. The concept was later extended to cover phenomena in nuclear physics and the physics of mesons and strange particles. One became accustomed to the idea of nuclear parities as well as atomic parities, and one discussed and measured the parities of mesons. Throughout these developments the concept of parity and the law of parity conservation proved to be extremely fruitful, and the success had in turn been taken as a support for the validity of right-left symmetry in physical laws.

In the years 1954–1956 a puzzle called the θ-τ puzzle developed. The θ and τ mesons are today known to be the same particle which is usually called K. In those years, however, one only knew that there were particles that disintegrate into two π mesons and particles that disintegrate into three π mesons. They were called respectively θ's and τ's, the τ being the name given to it by Powell in 1949. As time went on, measurements became more accurate and the increasing accuracy brought out more and more clearly a puzzlement. On the one hand it was clear that θ and τ had very accurately the same mass. They were also found to behave identically in other respects. So it looked as if θ and τ were really the same particle disintegrating in two different ways. On the other hand, increasingly accurate experiments also showed that θ and τ did not have the same parity and could not therefore be the same particle.

The resolution of the puzzle lay in a change in the concept of right-left symmetry. In the summer of 1956, T. D. Lee and I examined the then existing experimental foundation of this concept and came to the conclusion that, contrary to generally held belief, no experimental evidence of right-left symmetry actually existed for the weak interactions. If right-left symmetry does not hold for the weak interactions, the concept of parity is inapplicable to the decay mechanism of the θ and τ particles and they could therefore be one and the same particle, as we now know they are.

As a possible way out of the θ-τ puzzle, it was suggested that one should test experimentally whether right-left symmetry is violated for the weak interactions. The principle of the test is very simple: two sets of experimental arrangements which are mirror images of each other are set up. They must contain weak interactions and they must not be identical[12] to each other. One then examines whether the two arrangements always give the same results. If they do not, one would have an unambiguous proof of the violation of right-left symmetry in this experiment. In Figure 34 the first such experiment, performed by C. S. Wu, E. Ambler, R. W. Hayward, D. D. Hoppes, and R. P. Hudson in 1956, is schematically illustrated. The cobalt nuclei disintegrate by weak interactions and the disintegration products are counted. Notice

FIGURE 34, see next page

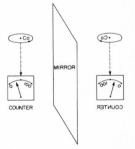

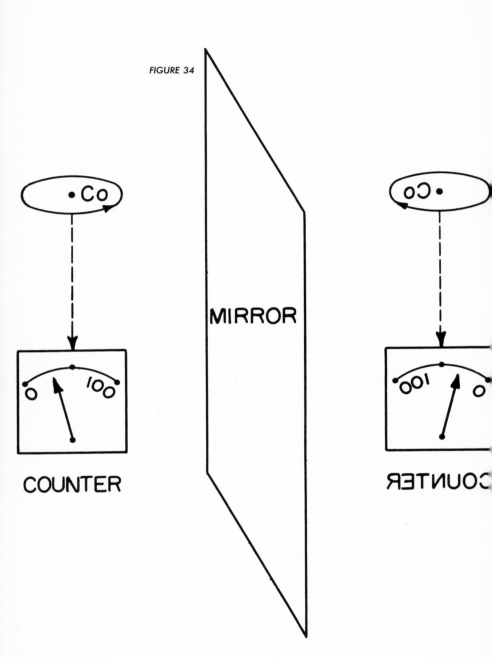

FIGURE 34

MIRROR

COUNTER

COUNTER

that the currents flowing in the loops are very
essential elements of the experiment. Without
these currents the two arrangements on the two
sides of the imagined mirror would have been
identical and would have always given the same
results. To make the influence of the currents
felt by the cobalt nuclei, however, it was necessary to eliminate the disturbance on the cobalt
produced by thermal agitations. The experiments had to be done, therefore, at extremely
low temperatures of the order of less than .01
degrees absolute. The technique of combining
β-disintegration measurements with low tem-
perature apparatus was a major difficulty. A
picture of the actual equipment is shown in
Figure 35. The cobalt sample was contained
in the tube in the foreground. The big magnet
in the background was part of the cooling
apparatus.

FIGURE 35

The result of the experiment was that there was a very large difference in the readings of the two meters shown in Figure 34. Since the behavior of the other parts of the apparatus observes right-left symmetry, the asymmetry must be attributed to the disintegration process of cobalt, which is due to a weak interaction.

Hermann Weyl said in his lectures[13] referred to above that in art "seldom is asymmetry merely the absence of symmetry." This seems also to hold in physics, for with the discovery of the lack of right-left symmetry there arose two new aspects concerning the right-left symmetry-asymmetry of the elementary particles and their interactions. The first has to do with the *structure of the neutrino* and very interestingly is a revival of an idea originally formulated by Weyl in 1929. It was, however, rejected in the past because it did not preserve right-left symmetry. Since the neutrino participates only in weak interactions, the overthrow of right-left symmetry in weak interactions invalidated this reason of rejection and revived Weyl's idea. Many experiments were done in 1957 on the neutrino and confirmed its predictions. Let us emphasize that Weyl's proposal was based on mathematical grounds of elegance and simplicity. It can hardly be an accident that nature again in this case, as in other cases, betrays her partiality for the beauty of mathematical reasoning.

The second aspect concerns the question whether right-left symmetry is really lost in the light of the new development. The very interesting point here is that if one changes one's definition of a mirror reflection, then mirror reflection symmetry could be restored. To explain this point let us denote the readings of the meters on the left and on the right of Figure 34 by L and R respectively. Let us further denote the readings of the same arrangements, but constructed with antimatter, by $\overline{L}$ and $\overline{R}$ respectively. Before the experiment of Wu, Ambler, Hayward, Hoppes, and Hudson, it was believed that

$$L = R, \text{ and } \overline{L} = \overline{R},$$

on grounds of right-left symmetry. Also it was believed that

$$L = \overline{L}, \text{ and } R = \overline{R},$$

on grounds of matter-antimatter symmetry. Consequently one believed that

$$L = R = \overline{L} = \overline{R}.$$

Their experiment demonstrated the fallacy of this belief by explicitly showing

$$L \neq R.$$

It can be proved from their quantitative results and from subsequent experiments in many laboratories that in fact

$$L = \overline{R} \neq \overline{L} = R.$$

There is thus clearly less symmetry than previously believed, but there is still *some* symmetry left in the relations

$$L = \overline{R}$$
$$\overline{L} = R.$$

Both of these can be summarized in the principle that if one performs a mirror reflection *and* converts all matter into antimatter, then physical laws remain unchanged. This combined transformation which leaves physical laws unchanged could thus be *defined* as the true mirror reflection process. According to this definition, mirror reflection symmetry is restored.

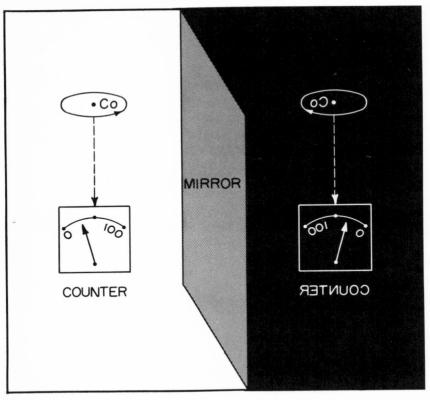

FIGURE 36   This new definition of mirror reflection is illustrated in Fig. 36 where antimatter is represented by white lines against a black background. In this figure the reading of the meter on the left is L, that of the meter on the right is $\overline{R}$. Experiments show that these two readings *are* the same.

Of course the question remains why it is necessary in order to have symmetry, to *combine* the operation of switching matter and antimatter with a mirror reflection. The answer to such a question can only be obtained through a deeper understanding of the relationship between matter and antimatter. No such understanding is in sight today. However, it is both interesting and useful to recall a somewhat similar question and its final resolution. We quote from Weyl's book *Symmetry:*

"Ernst Mach tells of the intellectual shock he received when he learned as a boy that a magnetic needle is deflected in a certain sense, to the left or to the right, if suspended parallel to a wire through which an electric current is sent in a definite direction. Since the whole geometric and physical configuration, including the electric current and the south and north poles of the magnetic needle, to all appearances, are symmetric with respect to the plane E laid through the wire and the needle, the needle should react like Buridan's ass between equal bundles of hay and refuse to decide between left and right, . . ." (See Figure 37.)

Mach's difficulty lies in the apparent reflection symmetry of the arrangement of Fig. 37 with respect to the plane E containing the wire and the magnetic needle. But a deeper *understanding of magnetism* showed that the symmetry is only apparent. A magnet is a magnet because it

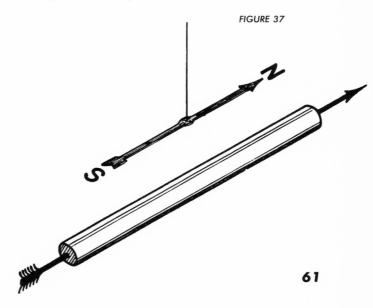

FIGURE 37

contains electrons making loop motions in the direction indicated in Fig. 38. Under a reflection, as indicated in that figure, the polarity of the magnet changes. Thus the reflection symmetry with respect to the plane E is not real, and Mach's difficulty is removed.

FIGURE 38

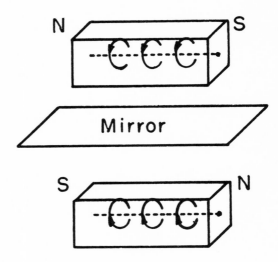

It is amusing to notice that symmetries that result under a combined transformation are well known in the decorative arts. In Figure 39 we reproduce a remarkable work of the Dutch artist, M. C. Escher. Notice that the picture is not identical to its mirror image. But if one switches the white and black colors of the mirror image, then identity is restored.

We have, in these discussions, taken a brief excursion in the field of physics of the last sixty years, following essentially the historical developments in elementary particle physics. No attempt was made to be complete in these discussions. Many discoveries of revolutionary

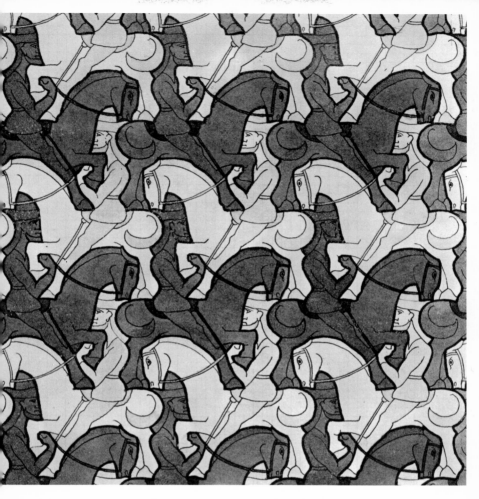

importance were thus not even mentioned. *FIGURE 39* Of those mentioned we could in all cases only touch upon the very beginning of the formation of the ideas, not their final fruition. Throughout these discussions our emphasis has been on the human experience in each period that had witnessed the evolution of the various ideas through the elaborate interplay between experimental reality and theoretical concepts. Merely for the sake of illustration the arguments and reasoning used have been qualitative in nature, but this should not be taken as a suggestion that new particles and new concepts are accepted in physics without detailed and quantitative formulation. Physics is a precise science and the physicists are deadly serious about their subject.

But what is the ultimate aim of the subject? Where does a physicist's vision lie? No one speaks with greater knowledge or greater authority on this topic than Einstein. He said that the aim of the subject is to construct concepts out of which a comprehensive workable system of theoretical physics can be formulated. The system must be as simple as possible, and yet must lead by deductive reasoning to conclusions that correspond with empirical experience. He wrote:[14]

"A complete system of theoretical physics is made up of concepts, fundamental laws which are supposed to be valid for those concepts and conclusions to be reached by logical deduction. It is these conclusions which must correspond with our separate experiences. . . .

The structure of the system is the work of reason; the empirical contents and their mutual relations must find their representation in the conclusions of the theory. In the possibility of such a representation lie the sole value and justification of the whole system, and especially of the concepts and fundamental principles which underlie it.

These fundamental concepts and postulates, which cannot be further reduced logically, form the essential part of a theory, which reason cannot touch. It is the grand object of all theory to make these irreducible elements as simple and as few in number as possible, without having to renounce the adequate representation of any empirical content whatever."

On the subject of the realizability of this grand object, he concluded:

" . . . , can we ever hope to find the right way? Nay more, has this right way any existence outside our illusions? Can we hope to be guided in the right way by experience when there exist theories (such as classical mechanics) which to a large extent do justice to experience, without getting to the root of the matter? I answer without hesitation that there is, in my opinion, a right way, and that we are capable of finding it. Our experience hitherto justifies us in believing that nature is the realisation of the simplest conceivable mathematical ideas. I am convinced that we can discover by means of purely mathematical constructions the concepts and the laws connecting them with each other, which furnish the key to the understanding of natural phenomena."

The faith so movingly expressed by Einstein still sustains the physicists today.

THE AUTHOR is indebted to the publishers and authors who generously gave permission to reproduce in this book figures from their publications or in their custody. These figures are listed below.

Fig. 1. J. J. Thomson, *Recollections and Reflections,* p. 325. Macmillan, New York (1937). Reproduced by permission of The Master and Fellows of Trinity College, Cambridge.

Fig. 2. Original photograph lent to Science Museum, London, by the late Lord Kelvin.

Fig. 3. J. J. Thomson, *Philosophical Magazine,* Vol. 44, p. 296 (1897).

Figs. 4, (26), 28, 29. J. J. Thomson, *Elektrizität und Materie,* Figs. 17, 18 and Table on p. 73. Braunschweig (1904).

Fig. 6. M. Born, *Restless Universe,* Fig. 77. Dover, New York (1951).

Fig. 7. J. Chadwick, *Proceedings of Royal Society,* London, Vol. A136, p. 695 (1932).

Fig. 8. Science Museum, London. Reproduced by permission of the Cavendish Laboratory, Cambridge.

Fig. 9. C. T. R. Wilson, *Proceedings of Royal Society,* London, Vol. A87, p. 278 (1912).

Fig. 10. Carl D. Anderson, *Physical Review,* Vol. 43, p. 492 (1933).

Fig. 12. A. M. Thorndike, *Mesons, A Summary of Experimental Facts,* Fig. 5. McGraw-Hill, New York (1952).

Fig. 13. C. F. Powell and G. P. S. Occhialini, *Nuclear Physics in Photographs,* Pls. XLIX and L. Clarendon Press, Oxford (1947).

Fig. 14. C. F. Powell, *Report on Progress in Physics,* Vol. 13, p. 384 (1950).

Fig. 16. A. M. Thorndike, *Mesons, A Summary of Experimental Facts,* Fig. 13. McGraw-Hill, New York (1952). This is a sketch of the original photograph in G. D. Rochester and C. C. Butler, *Nature,* Vol. 160, p. 855 (1947).

Fig. 17. R. Brown, U. Camerini, P. H. Fowler, H. Muirhead, C. F. Powell and D. M. Ritson, *Nature,* Vol. 163, p. 82 (1949).

Fig. 19. L. W. Alvarez.

Figs. 20, 21. Brookhaven National Laboratory.

Fig. 23. L. W. Alvarez.

Fig. 25. D. A. Glaser.

Fig. 27. J. J. Thomson, *Die Korpuskulartheorie der Materie,* Fig. 25. Braunschweig (1908).

Fig. 30. D. A. Glaser.

Fig. 31. W. B. Fowler, R. P. Shutt, A. M. Thorndike and W. L. Whittemore, *Physical Review,* Vol. 93, p. 863 (1954).

Fig. 32. H. Weyl, *Symmetry,* Fig. 67. Princeton University Press (1952). The original source of this figure is D. S. Dye, *A Grammar of Chinese Lattice,* Fig. C9b, Harvard Yenching Institute Monograph V, Cambridge (1937).

Fig. 33. H. Weyl, *Symmetry,* Fig. 45. Princeton University Press (1952). The original source of this figure is E. Haeckel, Challenger monograph, *Report on the Scientific Results of the Voyage of H.M.S. Challenger,* Vol. XVIII, Pl. 117. H.M.S.O. (1887).

Fig. 35. C. S. Wu, E. Ambler, R. W. Hayward, D. D. Hoppes and R. P. Hudson.

Fig. 37. H. Weyl, *Symmetry,* Fig. 14. Princeton University Press (1952).

Fig. 39. P. Terpstra, *Introduction to the Space Groups,* Wolters, Groningen (1955). The drawing was originally made by M. C. Escher.

FOOTNOTES

1. W. T. Kelvin, *Nature LVI,* 1897, p. 84.
2. J. J. Thomson, *Recollections and Reflections,* MacMillan Co., 1937, p. 334.
3. J. J. Thomson, *Phil. Mag. 44,* 1897, p. 293.
4. N. Bohr, *J. Chem. Soc.,* Feb. 1932, p. 349.
5. J. R. Oppenheimer, *Science and the Common Understanding,* Simon and Schuster, 1953.
6. Mev is the abbreviation of "million electron volts," representing the energy of an electric charge *e* raised to the potential of one million volts.
7. C. T. R. Wilson, Le Prix Nobel, 1927.
8. Y. Yukawa, "Collected Papers from Osaka University," II, 1935, p. 52.
9. See R. A. Millikan, *Electrons, Protons, Photons, Neutrons, Mesotrons and Cosmic Rays,* University of Chicago Press, 1947.
10. The disintegration products of π^-, μ^- and $\bar{n}$ are the antiparticles of the disintegration products of π^+, μ^+ and n:
$$\pi^- \rightarrow \mu^- + \bar{\nu},$$
$$\mu^- \rightarrow e^- + \bar{\nu} + \nu,$$
$$\bar{n} \rightarrow \bar{p} + e^+ + \nu.$$
11. F. M. Jaeger, *The Principle of Symmetry,* Amsterdam: Elsevier, 1920.
12. If the two arrangements are identical to each other, they would always give the same results and the experiments would not constitute a test of right-left symmetry.
13. H. Weyl, *Symmetry,* Princeton University Press, 1952.
14. A. Einstein, *Essays in Science,* Philosophical Library, 1934, pp. 14–15.

Spin[3]	Stra:
½	
½	
½	
½	
½	
½	
½	
½	
0	
0	
0	
0	
1	
½	unde
½	unde
½	unde

g sec.
$+ \pi^-, \pi^0 + \pi^0$;
s only one mean
d lifetimes. They
s of the disintegr